9·99.

AMAZING STUDIES

SAXOPHONE

Selected and arranged by Howard Harrison

BOOSEY

London · New

D0239477

▷INTRODUCTION

I have selected the pieces in *Amazing Studies* because they are enjoyable, 'real' pieces. They work without an accompaniment and have been arranged to help you improve your technique in the most enjoyable way. Here are a few general tips to help you get the most out of *Amazing Studies*:

• Try playing your instrument in a resonant room (one with an echo). A bare hallway or a kitchen will reward you with a more exciting sound than a room full of soft furnishings.

• Play rhythmically. There's no-one else to help you drive these pieces along, so you should stress the rhythm more than usual. It's more fun this way, and more expressive.

• Tune up carefully before you play. Even though you don't need to be in tune with anyone else, your instrument will produce its best tone at concert pitch.

• When you practise these studies, play them exactly as written. If you take care to play them slowly and accurately at first, with clean fingering, full tone, and accurate articulation, then playing them quickly will be no problem.

• Once you have mastered each study, try to play it more freely and expressively. Each one is more than just a study and should be enjoyed. As the jazz saxophonist Charlie Parker said, you should play every piece as if you own it.

• Try adding extra ornaments and melodic decorations to the baroque pieces (those by Bach, Telemann and Quantz). It was quite common for these composers to leave this sort of thing up to the player. The dynamics marked in these pieces are usually mine, so change them as you wish.

• I've suggested quite a lot of grace notes in the folk pieces - you can move or remove them, but most folk music sounds undressed without *any* ornament. The jigs, reels and hornpipes can be repeated as many times as you like: keep playing until you feel satisfied - every folk player has to find stylish solutions of their own.

You can use this book in three ways:

1 If you're simply looking for something new to play, browse until you find a piece that takes your fancy - and off you go.

2 If you're interested in developing or practising a particular skill, go to the index at the back of the book and look up, say, *staccato* - this will tell you which pieces are particularly useful as *staccato* studies, and in rough order of difficulty.

3 Having selected a piece, you might find that it features something that you find a little awkward - arpeggios, for instance, or syncopated rhythms. In the margins you might find some advice, along with arrows and numbers guiding you to similar pieces for extra practice.

⇩   guides you to easier pieces,

⇨   to pieces of the same difficulty level,

⇧   to harder pieces.

(piece numbers after the arrows are given in order of difficulty)

And when your unaccompanied playing sounds good, your accompanied playing will sound *Amazing*.

Howard Harrison, April 1997

CONTENTS

Jigs should skip along lightly, so keep your fingers close to the keys and the tonguing light. Aim for a relaxed sound.

1. The Butcher's March

traditional

G major ⇩37   ⇧2
agility ⇧21

2. I'll get married in my old clothes

traditional

G major ⇩1   ⇧3

This compilation © Copyright 1997 by Boosey & Hawkes Music Publishers Ltd

3. Garryowen

traditional

G major ⇩2 ⇧60

Make the syncopated notes this shape ⌐, not this shape ▪. If you don't, the rag-time rhythms will sound flatfooted. You'll also need to sort out chromatic scale fingerings for both pieces.

4. *World's Fair Rag*

Harvey Babcock

C major ⇩*21* ⇧*38, 73*
syncopation ⇩*12, 42* ⇧*5, 19*
chromatic runs ⇧*5*
triplets ⇨*10, 27*

5. *Ophelia Rag*   James Scott (adapted by H.H.)

Bb major ⇩22 ⇧54
chromatic runs ⇩4
syncopation ⇩4 ⇨19
agility ⇩22
⇨19, 38, 40, 55, 56, 60, 69, 72
⇧61 (vars 2, 5, 6, 9)
accents ⇩61 (var 4) ⇧54

6. Early one morning

traditional

There are all sorts of important skills to practise in these four tunes. *Early one morning* needs a well shaped legato and smooth tonguing.

B♭ major ⇨8 ⇧32
legato ⇧47, 48
legato tonguing ⇧68
consistency of tone
⇨8, 13, 25 ⇧36, 47, 48
warmth of tone ⇨8 ⇧27, 62

7. Sheffield Hornpipe

traditional

Sheffield Hornpipe and *Morpeth Rant* are full of standard F major and A major finger patterns and will help you practise your articulation.

F major ⇧20
accents ⇧61 (var 10)
swung rhythm ⇨23 ⇧21

8. *The Ash Grove*

traditional

The Ash Grove needs a subtle, "courtly" rhythmic style, a round warm tone and smooth scale fingering.

B♭ major ⇨6 ⇧32
consistency of tone ⇨6, 13, 25 ⇧36, 47, 48
warmth of tone ⇨6, 27 ⇧62
the break ⇨13

9. *Morpeth Rant*

traditional

A major ⇩47 ⇧46
agility ⇩21 ⇨20, 49 ⇧22

10. Study

Giuseppe Gariboldi

This very beautiful study has a distinctly Spanish flavour. Use *rubato* to make it more expressive and dramatic.

B minor ⇩36 ⇨50 ⇧75

triplets ⇨4, 27

expression ⇩34, 47 ⇨63, 67 ⇧33, 57

dynamics
⇩18 ⇨66 ⇧46, 57

rubato ⇨67 ⇧33

11. Study

Giuseppe Gariboldi

F minor ⇨40
expression ⇩33, 57   ⇨39, 69
mixed articulation
⇩46   ⇨19, 24, 26   ⇧54
dynamics
⇩46, 57   ⇨61 (var 7)
rubato ⇩33   ⇨61 (var 4), 69
⇧35 (Adagietto)
rising intervals ⇩32, 43

12. Ecco la primavera

Francesco Landini

In *Ecco la primavera,* all the bars are the same length, but bars 4, 7, 13, 14, 20 and 21 are in 6/8 rather than 3/4. Remember to accent the first and fourth ♪ in each of these bars.

syncopation ⇨ 42   ⇧ 4
unusual time signatures ⇧ 50, 62
mixed articulation ⇩ 41   ⇧ 31

13. Medieval Dance Tune

anonymous

C major ⇧ 74
the break ⇨ 8
consistency of tone ⇨ 6, 8, 25   ⇧ 36, 47, 48

14. *La rotta*

anonymous

D minor (dorian mode)
⇩15 ⇨28 ⇧33
strength of tone ⇩64 ⇧33

15. Bourrée (from Lute Suite in E Minor BWV 996)

J.S. Bach

Baroque composers often trusted players to phrase and decorate their music themselves, so many of the performance details here are left up to you. How would you articulate the repeated pattern in this piece? You don't have to use the same articulation all the way through.

D minor ⇧ 14, 28

16. Gigue (BWV 845)

attributed to J.S. Bach

Here's a piece that is already marked with phrasing and articulation, but you could still add some decorations of your own here and there.

A major ⇩46 ⇨69

"The Flute Master" is a collection of pieces from the 18th century, mostly anonymous, written for the instruction and entertainment of recorder players.

17. Song

anonymous

E minor ⇨ 29   ⇧ 42
dynamics ⇧ 18

18. Ghosts of ev'ry occupation

anonymous

G minor ⇨ 34, 43, 52   ⇧ 64
staccato ⇨ 52   ⇧ 46
dynamics ⇩ 17   ⇧ 10, 66

19. *Calypso Collapso*

Howard Harrison

A calypso is a kind of Caribbean song. It is full of syncopated rhythms which may look complicated on the page, but should sound natural.

E♭ major ⇓70
syncopation ⇓4 ⇨5
agility ⇓22
⇨5, 38, 40, 55, 56, 60, 69, 72
⇑61 (vars 2, 5, 6, 9, 11)
mixed articulation
⇓46 ⇨11, 24, 26 ⇑54

20. Londonderry Hornpipe

Irish traditional

At least three of these folktunes are well known on both sides of the Atlantic. To make a hornpipe rhythm, you'll need to give a slight push to the second and fourth beats of each bar.

F major ⇩7   ⇧72
swung rhythms ⇩21
⇨30, 49, 61 (var 8)   ⇧72, 73
agility ⇩21   ⇨9, 49   ⇧22

21. Redesdale Hornpipe

English traditional

C major ⇩23   ⇧4
swung rhythms ⇩7, 23
⇧20, 30, 49, 61 (var 8)
agility ⇩1   ⇧9, 20, 49

22. Bee's Wing Hornpipe

James Hill

B♭ major ⇩27, 49 ⇧5
agility ⇩9, 20, 49
⇧5, 19, 38, 40, 55,
56, 60, 69, 72

23. President Garfield

New England traditional

C major ⇩74 ⇧21
swung rhythm ⇨7 ⇧21

24. The Flower Drum Song

Chinese traditional arr. H.H.

Chinese music can sound optimistic, sweetly sentimental, energetic and passionate all at the same time.

non-western scales
⇩ 62, 63, 65

mixed articulation ⇩ 46
⇨ 11, 19, 26   ⇧ 54

25. Bamboo Flute

Chinese traditional arr. H.H.

non-western scales
⇧ 62, 63, 65

consistency of tone
⇨ 6, 8, 13   ⇧ 36, 47, 48

26. The Four Seasons

Chinese traditional arr. H.H.

A minor ⇩57
tonguing ⇨45, 40, 61 (var 4)
mixed articulation
⇩46   ⇨11, 19, 24   ⇧54
strength of tone ⇩33   ⇨51

Johann Joachim Quantz (1697-1773) was a great flute player and composer. His book "On Playing the Flute" tells us much of what we now know about the performance of Baroque music.

27. *Fantasia*

Johann Joachim Quantz

B♭ major ⇩ 32 ⇨ 49 ⇧ 22

triplets ⇨ 4, 10

warmth of tone
⇩ 6, 8 ⇨ 62 ⇧ 39

28. *Fantasia*

Johann Joachim Quantz

D minor ⇩15   ⇨14   ⇧33
slurred pairs ⇨59

29. Soldier's Joy

traditional

This tune is most often played in the major key - so try adding another three sharps for some E major practice!

E minor ⇨17   ⇧42

30. Sweep's Hornpipe

traditional

D major ⇩71   ⇨66
swung rhythms
⇩21   ⇨20, 49, 61 (var 8)
⇧72, 73

31. *Morgan Magan*

Turlough O' Carolan

Turlough O' Carolan was a blind Irish harpist of the 18th century. His music was influenced both by European music at the time as well as the folk music of his own country. Like a lot of his pieces, this is named after the person who asked him to write it.

C major ⇩23   ⇨21   ⇧4
mixed articulation ⇩12   ⇧66

23

32. Prelude

Nicolini Cosma

B♭ major ⇩ 6, 8   ⇧ 27, 49
rising intervals ⇨ 43   ⇧ 11

33. Swineherd's Dance I

Howard Harrison

These arrangements (continued over the page) are in the style of the Hungarian composer Béla Bartók. To get a sense of how they should be played, listen to some of his arrangements of folk-songs - or some Balkan folk music.

D minor (dorian mode)
⇩14, 28   ⇧39, 51, 58
expression ⇩10, 63, 67
⇨57   ⇧11, 39, 69
rubato ⇩10, 67
⇧11, 61 (var 4), 69
strength of tone ⇩14
⇧26, 51

34. Bride's Candle Dance

Howard Harrison

G minor ⇨ 18, 43, 52   ⇧ 64
expression ⇨ 47   ⇧ 10, 63, 67

35. Round Dance & Swineherd's Dance II

Howard Harrison

E minor (dorian mode)
⇩42 ⇨61
F♯ minor (dorian mode) ⇩44
tempo changes ⇩67
metre changes ⇩54 ⇨75
rubato ⇩11, 61 (var 4), 69
mixed articulation
⇩54 ⇨61 (var 5)
mixed ornaments ⇩51, 76

36. Epping Forest

anonymous

B minor ⇧10, 50
consistency of tone
⇩6, 8, 13, 25   ⇨47, 48   ⇧59

37. Jig

Howard Harrison

In this piece, keep your fingering even and use some light breath accents within the slurs. This will give it lots of impetus and energy.

G major ⇧1

38. *Allegro* (from *Fantaisie* for solo violin)   Georg Philipp Telemann

C major ⇩4
agility ⇩22
⇨5, 19, 40, 55, 56, 60, 69, 72
⇧61 (vars 2, 5, 6, 9, 11)

39. Malle Symen

Jacob van Eyck

Jacob van Eyck (1589-1657) was a blind musician from Utrecht. He sometimes played recorder in a church-yard to amuse passers-by. Play these pieces freely and try to make them sound improvised.

Malle Symen contains a number of phrases which are immediately repeated an octave lower; try to balance the volume and tone in the two registers so that the reply doesn't sound weak.

D minor ⇓33   ⇨51, 58   ⇧75
expression ⇓33, 57   ⇨11, 69
balancing registers ⇓52   ⇧44

40. Prins Robberts Masco

Jacob van Eyck

F minor ⇨11
agility ⬇22
⇨5, 19, 38, 55, 56, 60, 69, 72
⬆61 (vars 2, 5, 6, 9, 11)
large intervals ⬇61 (var 10)
⇨61 (var 3)   ⬆44
tonguing ⇨26, 45, 61 (var 4)

John Playford (1623-1686) was a London music publisher. These three tunes come from his book "The English Dancing Master", a collection of music and instructions for dancing.

D major ⇧71
mixed articulation ⇧12

41. The 29th of May

anonymous

42. Well's Humour (Purcell's Hornpipe)

Syncopated three-in-a-bar hornpipes like this one have survived mainly in the north-east of England - elsewhere they usually have two or four beats in the bar.

E minor ⇩17, 29   ⇧35, 61
syncopation ⇨12   ⇧4

43. *The Emperor of the Moon*

anonymous

This is a quirky
and earthy dance
tune. Be careful
not to let the tone
get coarse or the
rhythms flat-
footed.

G minor ⇨ *18, 34, 52*   ⇧ *64*
large intervals
⇨ *47*   ⇧ *61 (var 10)*
rising intervals ⇨ *32*   ⇧ *11*
balancing registers ⇧ *52*

With so many large leaps, this piece could easily sound disjointed. However, if you try playing all the notes below the C♯ on the third space an octave higher than written, you will hear that it is really a simple, flowing melody. It is just as simple but even more beautiful in the "expanded" version if you carry the melody across the large leaps without sudden changes of volume and tone.

F♯ minor ⇓45 ⇑35

large intervals
⇓40 (var 2), 61 (var 3)
⇑61 (vars 2, 5)
balancing registers ⇓39
consistency of tone ⇓52

44. Largo (from *Fantaisie* for solo violin) Georg Philipp Telemann

45. Vivace (from *Fantaisie* for solo violin) Georg Philipp Telemann

F♯ minor ⇑44
tonguing ⇒26, 40, 61 (var 4)

46. *Allegro*

Joseph Haydn

A major ⇩9   ⇧16, 69
mixed articulation
⇩66   ⇧11, 19, 24, 26
dynamics ⇩10, 66
⇨57   ⇧11, 61 (var 7)
staccato ⇩18, 52
⇧53, 61 (var 4)

47. The flower among them all

Sir Robert Fenwick

These two beautiful airs should be treated freely and imaginatively, as if you were improvising them.

A major ⇧9
expression
⇨34   ⇧10, 63, 67
large intervals ⇨43
⇧61 (var 10)
legato ⇩6   ⇨48   ⇧63
consistency of tone
⇩6, 8, 13, 25
⇨36, 48   ⇧59

48. The young black cow

traditional

A minor ⇧31

legato ⇩6 ⇨47 ⇧63

consistency of tone
⇩6, 8, 13, 25
⇨36, 47 ⇧59

49. Arthur Seat

James Scott Skinner

Arthur Seat is a hornpipe with a hint of ragtime about it, by the prolific and inventive Scottish fiddler, James Scott Skinner.

B♭ major ⇩32 ⇨27 ⇧22
agility ⇩21 ⇨9, 20 ⇧22
swung rhythms ⇩21
⇨20, 30, 49, 61 (var 8)
⇧72, 73

50. *La danse de Cleves*

anonymous

All the bars in this piece are the same length, but bars 15, 25, 29 and 33 are in 6/8 rather than 3/4. Remember to accent the first and fourth ♪ in each of these bars.

B minor ⇩36 ⇨10 ⇧75
unusual time signatures
⇩12 ⇨62 ⇧58

51. Trotto

anonymous

This piece was originally written down without bar lines. Some have been added to show how the melody should be accented, but you could try putting the bar lines where you think they fit best.

D minor ⇩33 ⇨39, 58 ⇧75
mixed ornaments ⇨76 ⇧35
changing metres ⇩65 ⇧54
strength of tone ⇩33 ⇨26

52. *Badine* (from *Picnic Suite*)

Claude Bolling

G minor ⇨ *18, 34, 43*   ⇧ *64*
staccato ⇨ *18*   ⇧ *46*
balancing registers
⇩ *43*   ⇧ *39*

53. *Rag-Polka* (from *Toot Suite*)

Claude Bolling

Badine Copyright © 1980 CAID MUSIC, *Rag-Polka* and *Spirituelle* Copyright © 1982 CAID MUSIC.
International Copyright Secured. All Rights Reserved

54. *Spirituelle* (from *Toot Suite*)

Claude Bolling

Vivace ♩ = c. 108

A♭ major ⇨ 55

staccato ⇩ 46 ⇨ 61 (var 4)
⇧ 61 (vars 2, 6, 7)

Each 9/4 bar subdivides into 4 + 3 + 2 rather than 3 + 3 + 3. Accent the subdivisions as if they were actual bars of 4, 3 and 2, but remember that the accidentals last to the end of each 9 beat cycle.

B♭ major ⇩ 5

unusual time signatures ⇩ 58
⇧ 61 (vars 2, 3, 4, 5, 6)
accents ⇩ 5
mixed articulation
⇩ 11, 19, 24, 26
⇧ 35, 61 (var 5)
changing metres
⇩ 51 ⇧ 35, 75

55. *Bourrée* (from Suite no. 3 in C major BWV 1009)

J.S. Bach

A♭ major ⇨ 53

agility ⇩ 22
⇨ 5, 19, 38, 40, 56, 60, 69, 72
⇧ 61 (vars 2, 5, 6, 9, 11)

56. *Gigue* (from Suite no. 1 in G major BWV 1007)

J.S. Bach

agility ⇩22
⇨5, 19, 38, 40, 55, 60, 69, 72
⇧61 (vars 2, 5, 6, 9, 11)

57. Hungarian Song

traditional arr. H.H.

A minor ⇓31 ⇑26
expression ⇓10, 63, 67
⇒33 ⇑11, 39, 69
dynamics ⇓10, 66 ⇒46
⇑11, 61 (var 7)

58. Bulgarian Dance

traditional arr. H.H.

The accents in this tune must be
1-2-**1**-2-3-**1**-2-**3**-4
all the way through - and remember that it is a dance.

D minor ⇓33 ⇒39, 51 ⇑75
acciaccaturas ⇓63 ⇑75
unusual time signatures ⇓50, 62 ⇑54

59. Soave (from *Fantaisie* for solo violin)

Georg Philipp Telemann

60. *Allegro* **(from *Fantaisie* for solo violin)**   Georg Philipp Telemann

G minor ⇩64 ⇨67
slurred pairs ⇨28
consistency of tone
⇩36, 47, 48 ⇧44

G major ⇩3

There is a long tradition of writing variations on "La folia", a very simple tune with a satisfying chord sequence. My variations are in lots of different styles and feature plenty of opportunities to improve your skills. They can be played as separate studies, or as one long performance piece. If you play them as one piece, follow the tempo indications and other markings carefully, to give the whole a good shape and sense of direction.

E minor ⇩42 ⇨35

multiple grace notes
⇨61 (var 8, coda)

unusual time signatures
⇩54 ⇨61 (vars 3, 4, 5, 6)

staccato ⇩53, 61 (var 4)
⇨61 (vars 6, 7)

agility ⇩5, 19, 38, 40, 55, 56, 60, 69, 72 ⇨61 (vars 5, 6, 9, 11)

large intervals
⇩44 ⇨61 (var 5)

61. 11 Variations on "La folia"

Howard Harrison

legato ⇩63

large intervals ⇩61 (var 10)
⇨40 (var 2) ⇧44

4. Scherzo alcoholico ♩ = c. 120

sempre stacc. e rubato

5. Scherzo grazioso

a tempo

staccato ⇩46 ⇨53
⇧61 (vars 2, 6, 7)
rubato ⇩33 ⇨11, 69
⇧35 (Adagietto)
tonguing ⇨26, 45, 40

large intervals
⇩44 ⇨61 (var 2)
mixed articulation ⇩54 ⇨35
agility ⇩5, 19, 38,
40, 55, 56, 60, 69, 72
⇨61 (vars 2, 6, 9, 11)

staccato ⇩53, 61 (var 4)
⇨61 (vars 2, 7)

unusual time signatures
⇩54   ⇨61 (vars 2, 3, 4, 5)

agility ⇩5, 19, 38,
40, 55, 56, 60, 69, 72
⇨61 (vars 2, 5, 9, 11)

staccato ⇩53, 61 (var 4)
⇨61 (vars 2, 6)

dynamics ⇩46, 57   ⇨11

swung rhythms ⇩21
⇨20, 30, 49   ⇧72, 73

agility ⇩5, 19, 38,
40, 55, 56, 60, 69, 72
⇨61 (vars 2, 5, 6, 11)

large intervals ⇩43, 47
⇧40 (var 2), 61 (var 3)
accents ⇩7   ⇧5

agility ⇩5, 19, 38,
40, 55, 56, 60, 69,
72, 61 (vars 2, 5, 6, 9)

multiple grace notes
⇨61 (var 1, 8)

62. *Jasmine Flower*

Pakistani traditional

mp sempre legato, molto rubato, espressivo

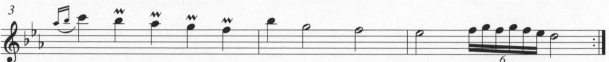

non-western scales
⇩25 ⇨63, 65 ⇧24
warmth of tone
⇩6, 8 ⇨27 ⇧39
unusual time signatures
⇩12 ⇨50 ⇧58

63. *Lovely Maiden*

Iraqi traditional arr. H.H.

non-western scales
⇩25 ⇨62, 65 ⇧24
legato ⇩47, 48 ⇧61 (var 3)
expression ⇩34, 47
⇨10, 67 ⇧33, 57
acciaccaturas ⇧58

64. *Tsur mishelo*

Israeli traditional

G minor ⇩*18, 34, 43, 52*
⇧*59, 67*

strength of tone ⇧*14*

65. *Hineh mah tov*

Jewish traditional

non-western scales ⇩*25*
⇨*62, 63* ⇧*24*

changing metres ⇧*51*

66. *Freilach*

Jewish traditional

This is a Jewish dance tune often played at weddings. The title is like the German word "fröhlich" which means "happy".

D major ⇩71 ⇨30
mixed articulation
⇩31 ⇧46
dynamics ⇩18
⇨10 ⇧46, 57

These three pieces should be played expressively - use *rubato* and changes of tone colour and tempo to bring out their changing moods.

A *barcarola* is a type of song used by Venetian gondoliers. The 6/8 time signature is meant to suggest the lilting movement of the boat through the water.

G minor ⇩64   ⇧59
expression ⇩34, 47
⇨10, 63   ⇧33, 57
rubato ⇨10   ⇧33
tempo changes ⇧35

67. Barcarola

Ernesto Köhler

68. Study

Ernesto Köhler

69. *Waltz*

Ernesto Köhler

C minor ⇨ 76
legato tonguing ⇩ 6

A major ⇩ 46 ⇨ 16
expression ⇩ 33, 57 ⇨ 11, 39
rubato ⇩ 33 ⇨ 11, 61 (var 4)
⇧ 35 (Adagietto)
agility ⇩ 22
⇨ 5, 19, 38, 40,
55, 56, 60, 72
⇧ 61 (vars 2, 5, 6, 9, 11)

An *estampie* is a kind of medieval instrumental music which may have been used for dancing. Each of these two pieces is made up of four sections. Play each section twice, the first time using ending **1**, the second time, using ending **2**.

70. La quinte estampie real

anonymous

E♭ major ⇧ 19

71. Salterello

anonymous

D major ⇩41   ⇨30, 66

72. J is 3

Howard Harrison

F major ⇩20

swung rhythms
⇩20, 30, 49, 61 (var 8)   ⇨73

agility ⇩22
⇨5, 19, 38, 40, 55, 56, 60, 69
⇧61 (vars 2, 5, 6, 9, 11)

73. *Jazz Etude no. 2*

Oscar Peterson

C major ⇓4 ⇨38
swung rhythms
⇓20, 30, 49, 61 (var 8) ⇨72

74. *Auvergne Polka*

French traditional

C major ⇩13 ⇧23

75. *Laride à six temps*

French traditional arr. H.H.

Depending on how you choose to play it, this tune can either be rousing or rather delicate and wistful. Either way, the ever-changing metres add to the restless beauty of the piece, so accent them clearly.

B minor ⇩ 10, 50
D minor ⇩ 39, 51, 58
changing metres ⇩ 54   ⇨ 35
acciaccaturas ⇩ 58

76. *La fille au cresson*

French traditional arr. H.H.

C minor ⇨ 68
mixed ornaments ⇨ 51   ⇧ 35

▷INDEX

This index provides a starting point to help you explore *Amazing Studies*. Although it is not exhaustive, it covers most of the common technical difficulties which this book can help you to practise.

Studies are listed under each heading by number, and in order of difficulty.

Cover design by Malcolm Stretten

Music setting by Halstan & Co. Ltd.

Reproduced and printed by Halstan & Co. Ltd., Amersham, Bucks., England